# FRUITS

GRAPES
GRAPES
GRAPES

# PEACH

PEACH

PEACH

**WATERMELON**

WATERMELON

WATERMELON

PEAR

PEAR

PEAR

**PINEAPPLE**

PINEAPPLE

PINEAPPLE

ORANGE
ORANGE
ORANGE

PLUM

PLUM

PLUM

LEMON

LEMON

LEMON

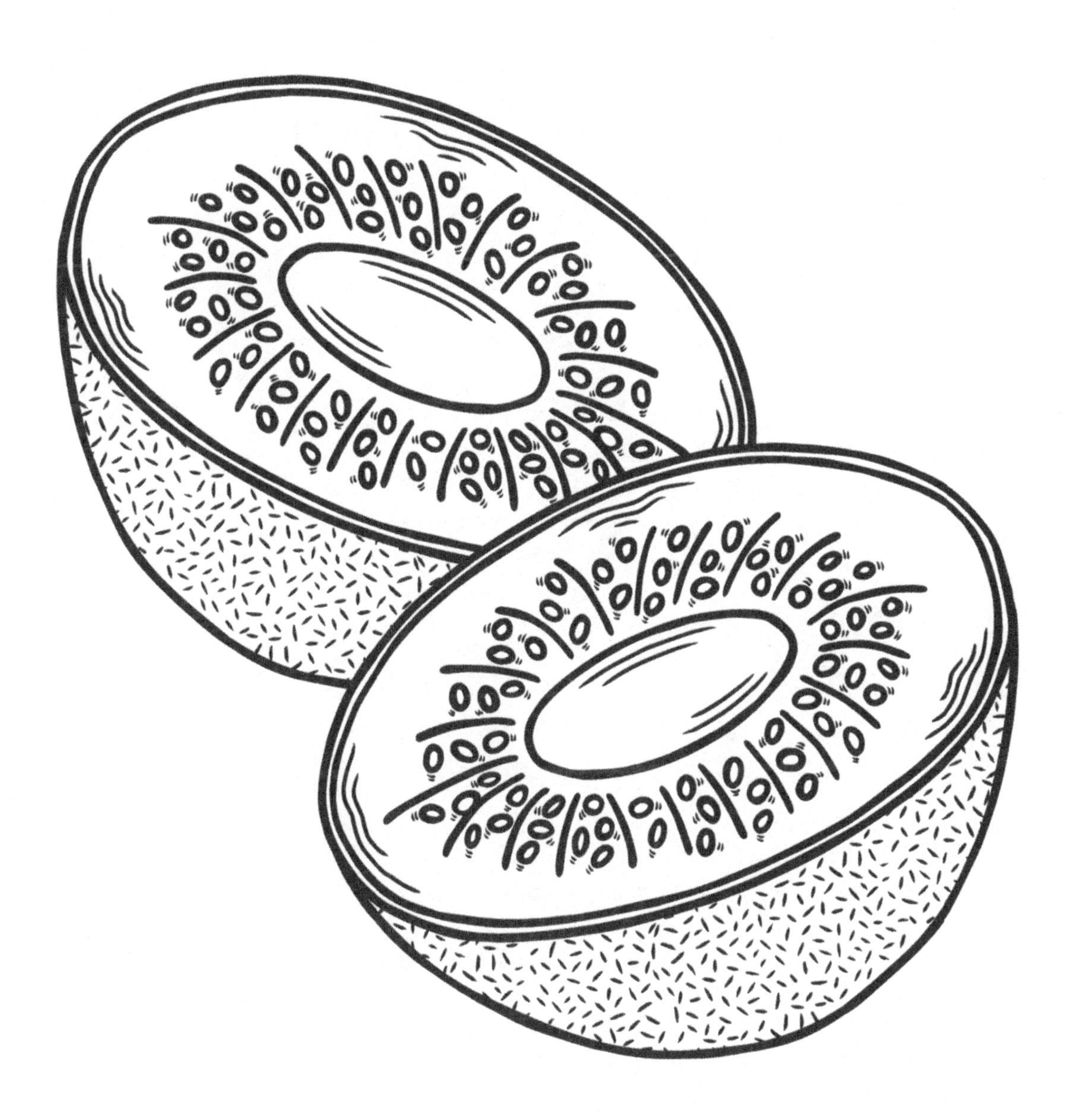

# KIWI

KIWI

KIWI

**STRAWBERRY**

STRAWBERRY

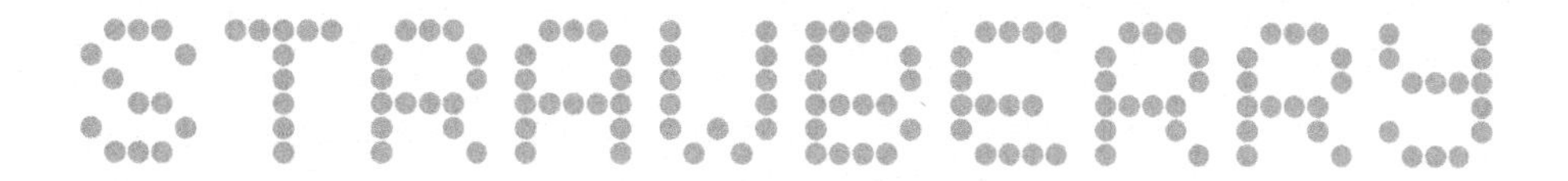

COCONUT

COCONUT

COCONUT

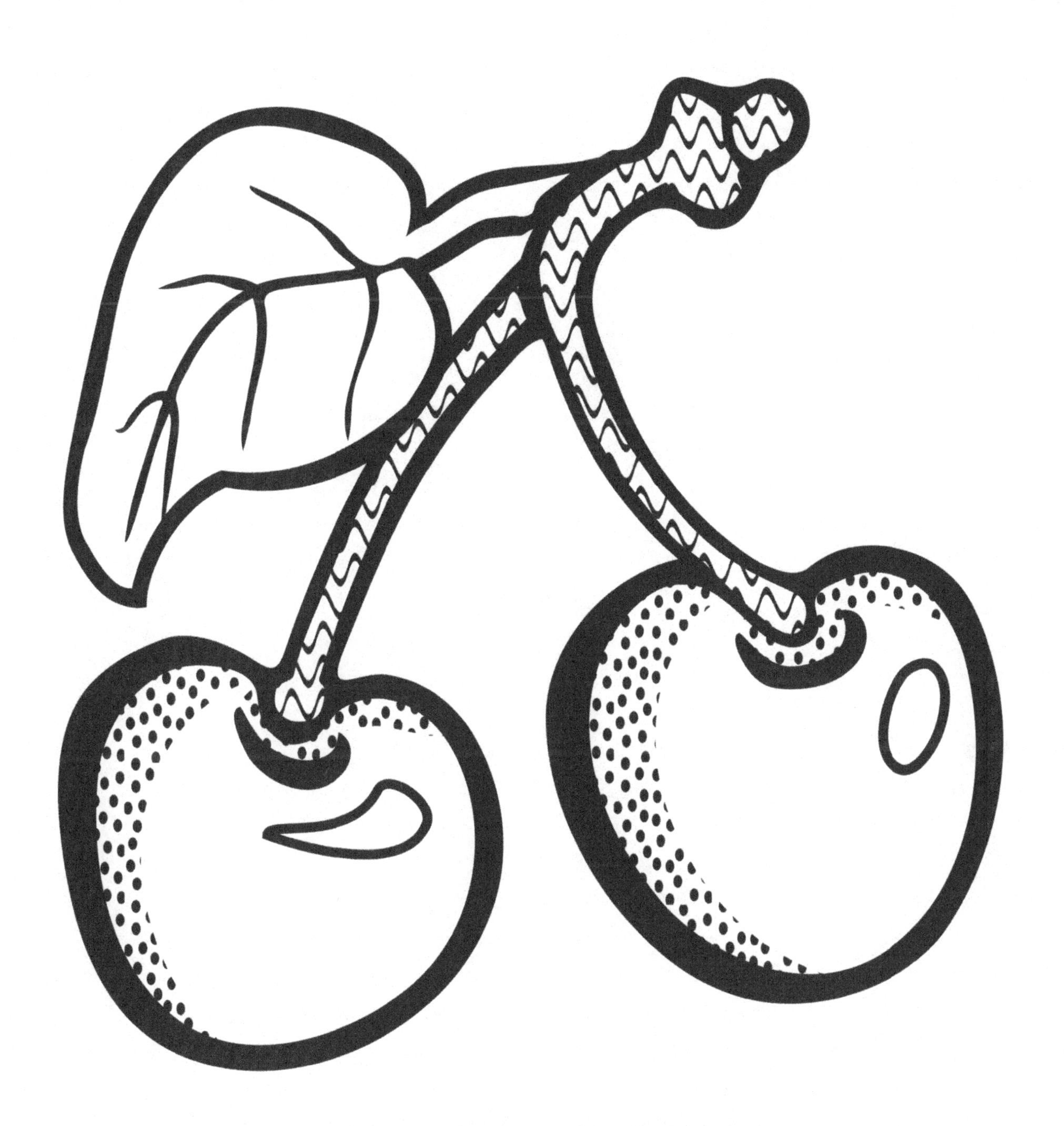

CHERRIES

CHERRIES

CHERRIES

BANANA

BANANA

BANANA

**APPLE**

APPLE

APPLE

FIGS

FIGS

FIGS

# POMEGRANATE

POMEGRANATE

POMEGRANATE

RASPBERRY

RASPBERRY

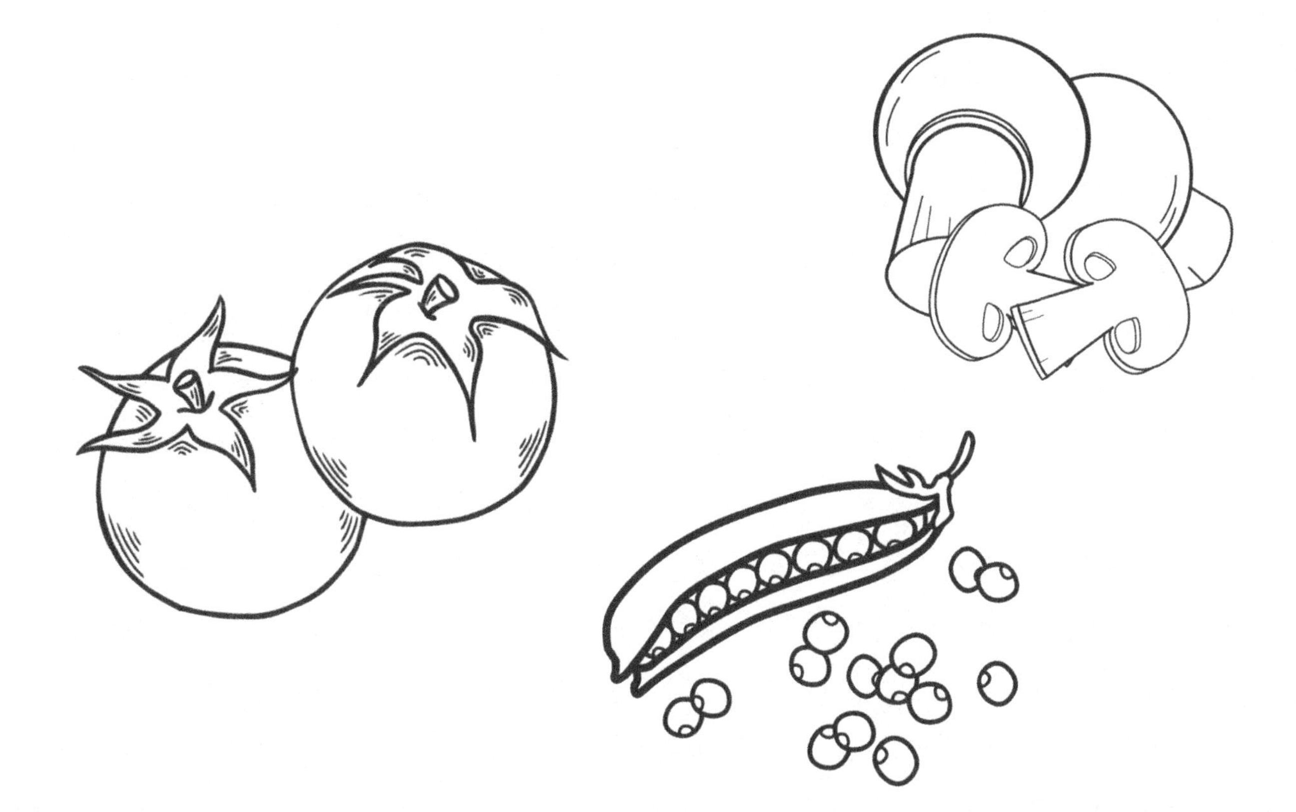

# VEGETABLES

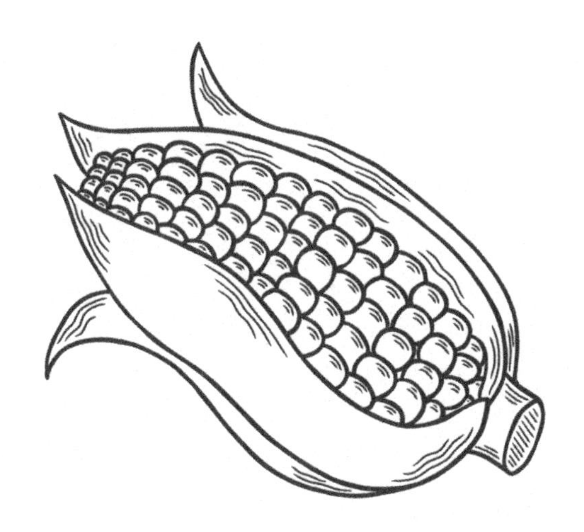

# CARROT

CARROT

CARROT

**TOMATO**
TOMATO
TOMATO

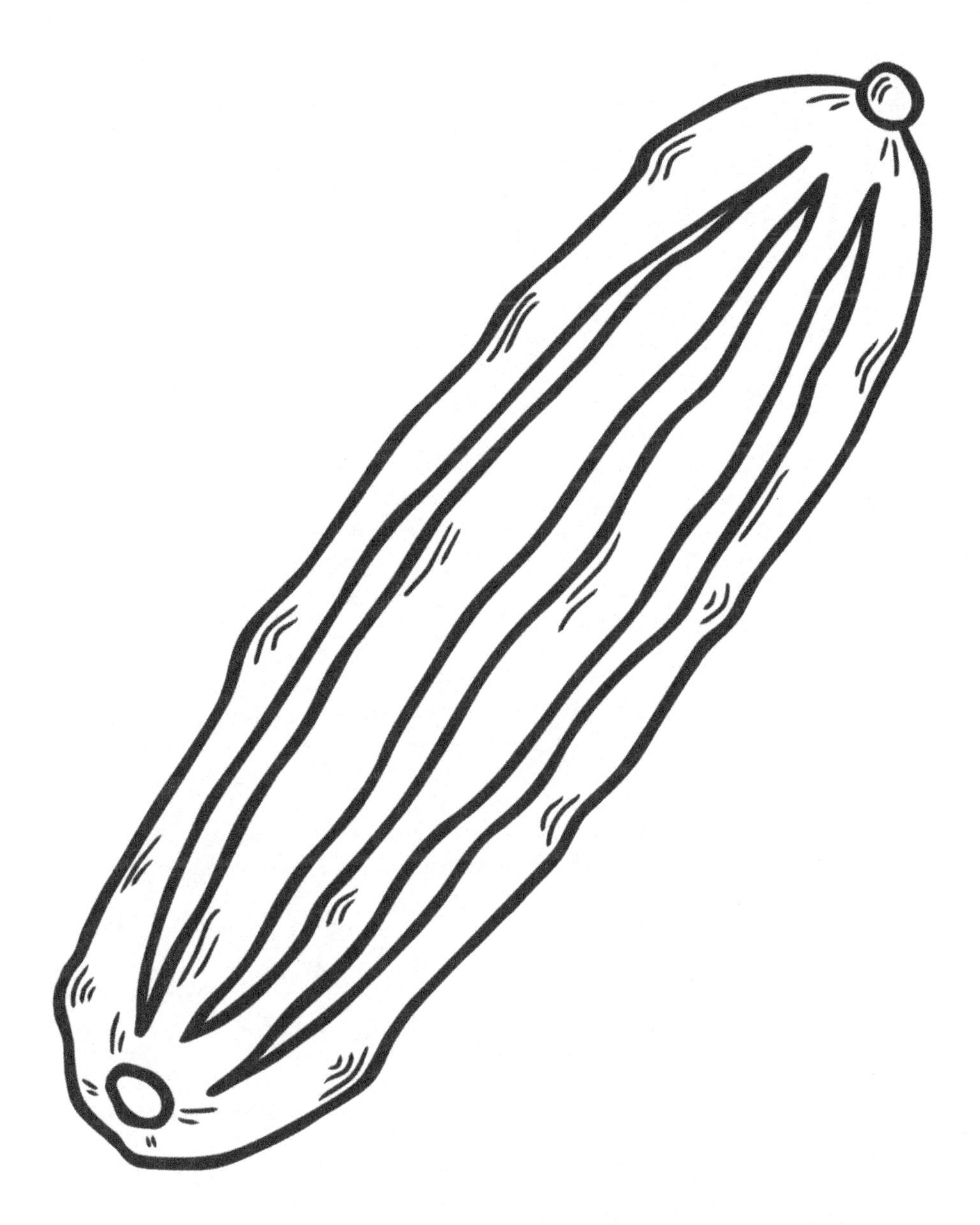

CUCUMBER

CUCUMBER

CUCUMBER

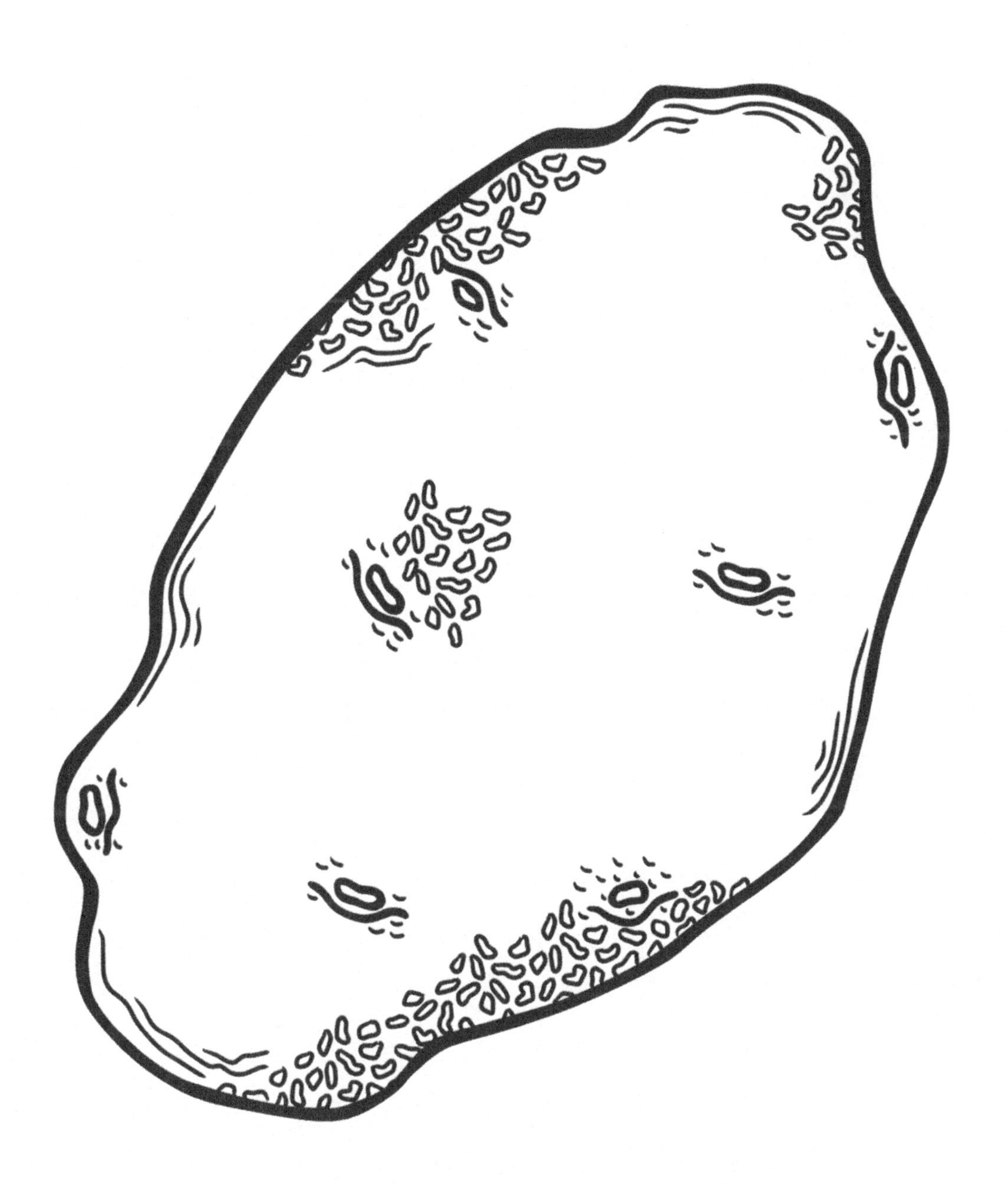

POTATOE

POTATOE

POTATOE

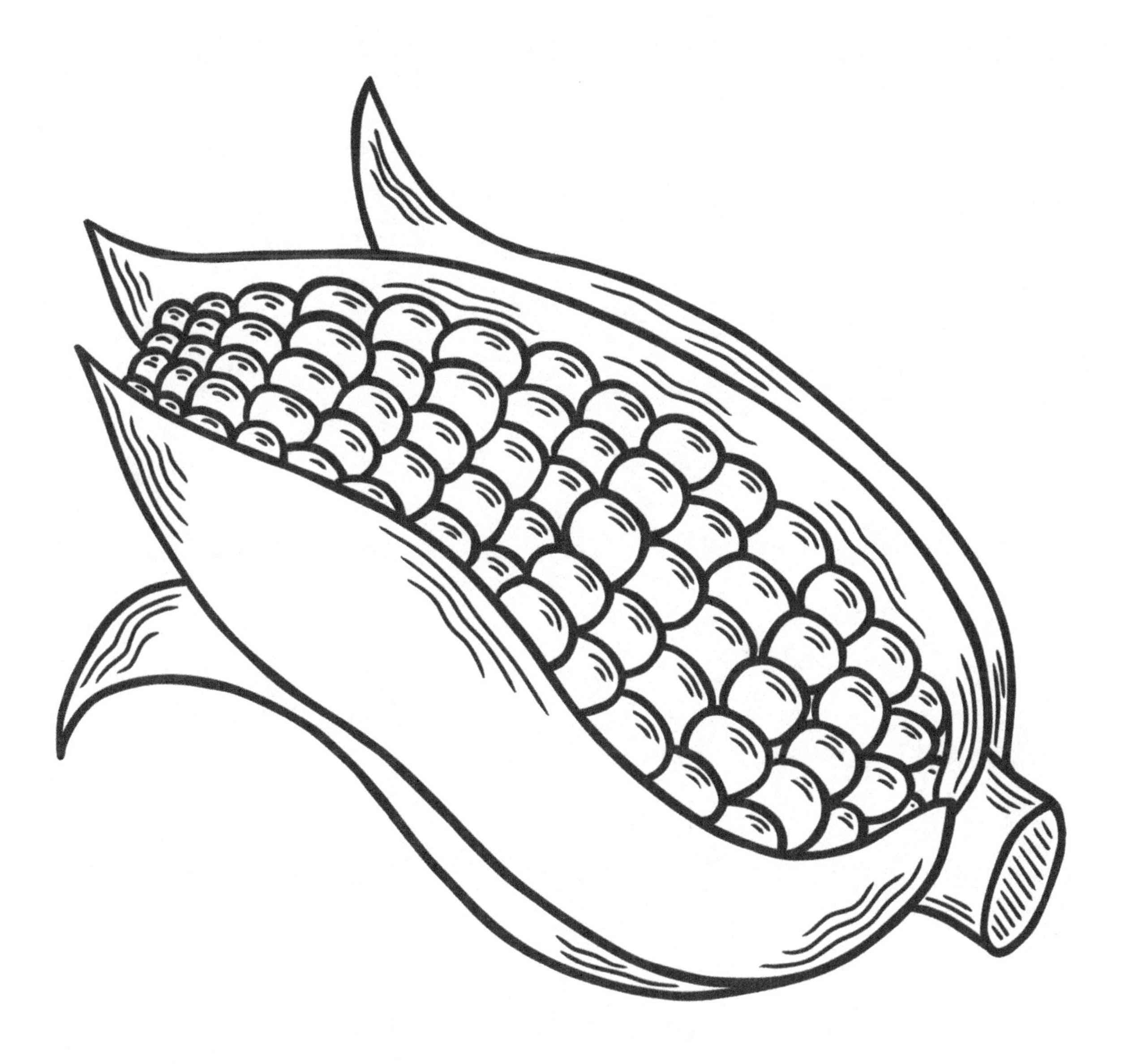

**CORN**

CORN

CORN

**LETTUCE**

LETTUCE

LETTUCE

PEAS

PEAS

PEAS

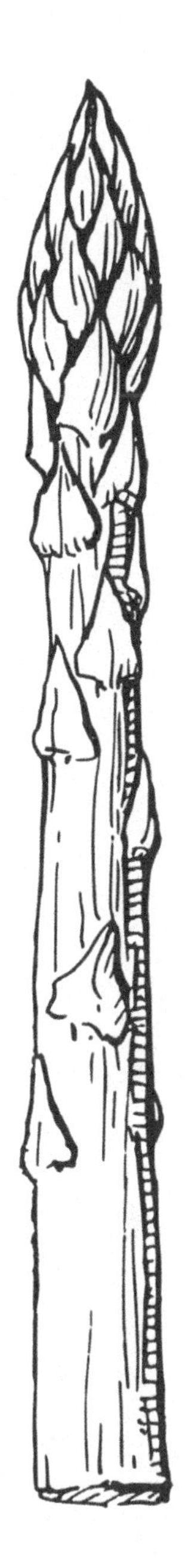

ASPARAGUS
ASPARAGUS
ASPARAGUS

MUSHRUMS

MUSHRUMS

MUSHRUMS

**BEET**

BEET

BEET

CABBAGE

CABAGGE

CABAGGE

ONION

ONION

ONION

PUMPKIN

PUMPKIN

PUMPKIN

BROCCOLI

BROCCOLI

BROCCOLI

EGGPLANT

EGGPLANT

EGGPLANT

# ARTICHOKE

ARTICHOKE

ARTICHOKE

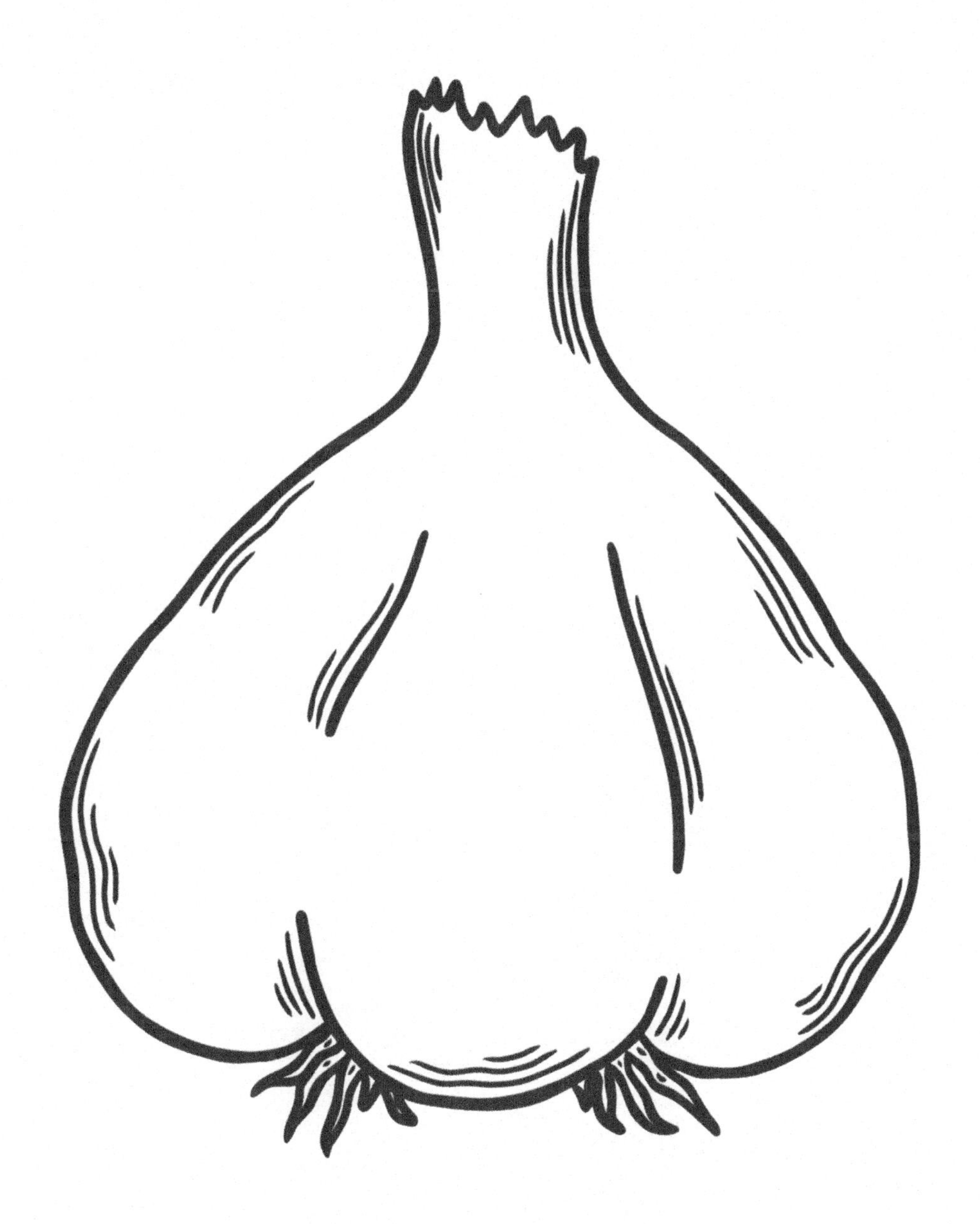

# GARLIC

GARLIC

GARLIC

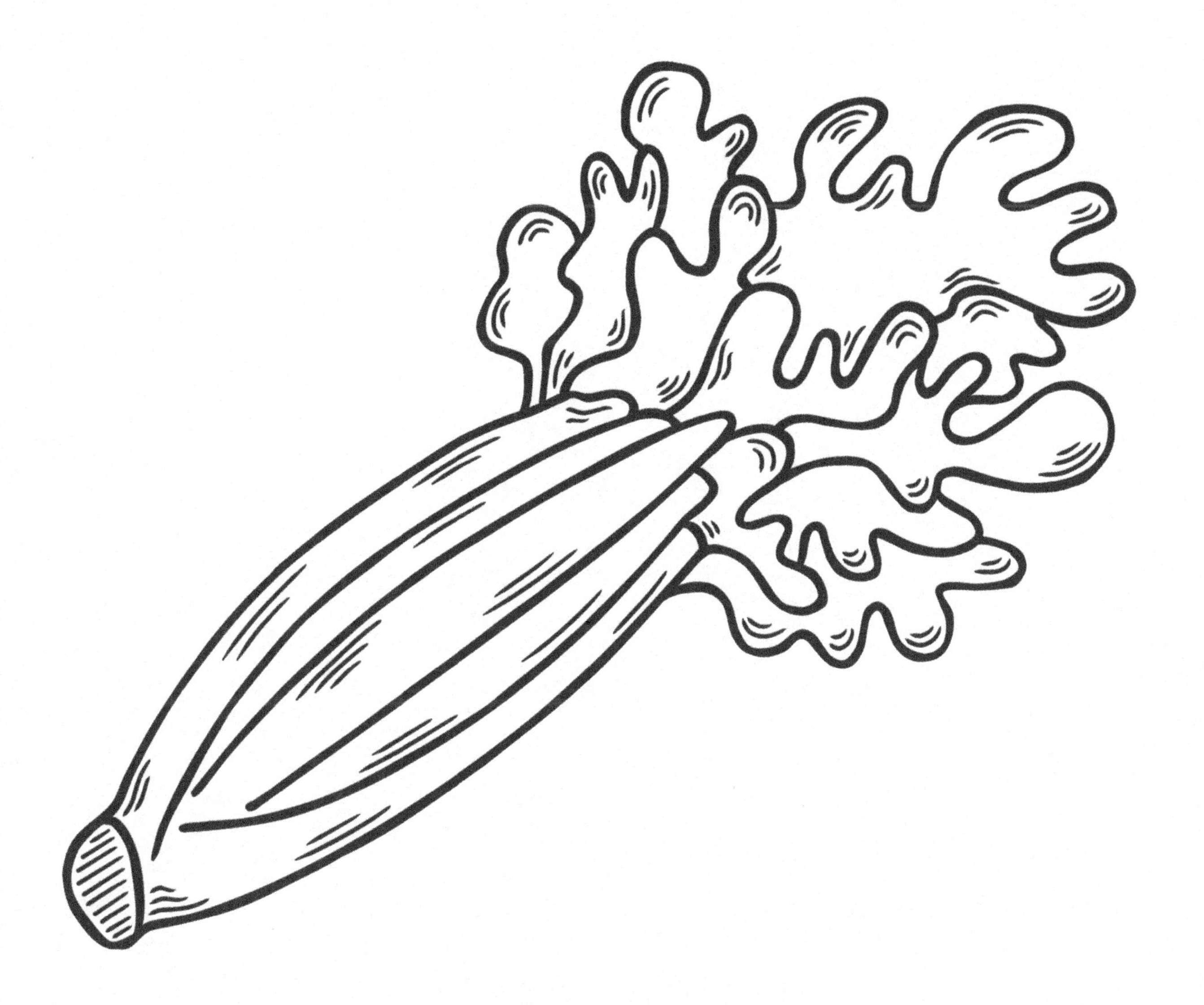

CELERY

CELERY

CELERY

CAULIFLOWER

CAULIFLOWER

CAULIFLOWER

# ZUCCHINI

ZUCCHINI

ZUCCHINI

Made in the USA
Monee, IL
02 August 2024

63158315R00044